KNOW PRACTICAL HORSE FEEDING

Charles W. Conrad, Editor
THE FARNAM HORSE LIBRARY

HORSE LIBRARY

The Farnam Horse Library
8701 North 29th Street
Omaha, Nebraska 68112

FRONT COVER
Here is a good example of what pasture feeding can do for your horse. This fine looking registered Arabian, Taroni, was photographed by Miss Judy Bleifus of Everett, Washington.

PHOTOGRAPH ACKNOWLEDGMENTS:
Mickles Valley View Ranch, Scottsdale, Arizona; Mills Ranch, Inc., Walsenburg, Colorado; Hillcroft Acres, Golden, Colorado; Hollywood Turf Club, Inglewood, California; Triple S Horse Farm, Glendale, Arizona; J. Warren Evans, Ph.D., University of California, Davis; State of Kentucky, Department of Public Information; C. C. Beck, D.V.M., Parke-Davis & Company, Detroit, Michigan; Earl L. Drake, D.V.M., Cooperative Extension Service, Reno, Nevada.

CONTENTS

KNOW PRACTICAL HORSE FEEDING

A human being with a hearty appetite is often said to "eat like a horse." The comparison may not always be an apt one, for many horses eat none too well. That's usually the fault of the owners, who don't pay enough attention to feeding. You are careful of your own diet, knowing that "you are what you eat." The same is true of your horse.

The rules aren't really so terribly complicated. You don't have to be a specialist. A few basic facts, coupled with a little "horse sense," should enable you to feed your horse successfully. Although the answers are simple, the whole subject is very important. Unless your horse is fed properly, his functions will be impaired—growth, reproduction, metabolism.

Feed a horse properly, and he will have animation, nerve, speed and endurance. Feed the same horse improperly, and he will be slow, dull and weak. Sometimes a small change in the ration produces a big effect on the animal's condition.

Feeding also has a large effect on your pocketbook. On the average, 50% of your expenditures on a horse go for his food. A horse owner may spend as much as $360 a year for feed. A working knowledge of alternative rations may well achieve the same results and save you $100 a year. Health for your horse, savings for you; that should be an ideal combination.

What is the best horse feed? How much should you feed? How often? Should you feed a vitamin supplement? These are important questions. The answers are in this volume. You are the chef for your horse; this is your cookbook. ■

CHAPTER ONE

THE DIGESTIVE SYSTEM

People aren't the only creatures with sensitive stomachs. A horse may be even more affected by his digestion than you are. To begin with, his digestive system is a huge undertaking; beginning at the mouth, it's a muscular tube over a hundred feet long, lined with mucous membranes.

There is a close relationship between these membranes and the horse's skin. Digestive disturbances may produce skin irritations; and it works the other way, too, because a bad skin condition can cause a digestive upset.

It is a complex mechanism. Between the mouth and the anus are the esophagus, the stomach, the small intestine, the large intestine and the rectum. Everything has to work together in peace to maintain good health. Then there are the various accessory organs, such as the teeth, salivary glands, liver and pancreas; they're all involved in the processing of food.

As with any animal, the function of the system is to break down the raw food into simpler chemical substances that can be absorbed by the blood stream. Most of these substances are water-soluble, so they can be absorbed through the lining of the mucous membrane. Glucose, salt, water and a few more, can be absorbed without chemical change.

Let's take time to explore your horse's digestive system. Since chewing is the first step in the process, our starting point is obvious.

The Mouth

If it's authoritative, then it's "straight from the horse's mouth." It will be interesting to see just what that symbol of truth is really like.

A horse's mouth is usually described as starting with the lips and ending with the pharynx. On the sides are the cheeks; above is the hard palate; below is the tongue. At the rear is the soft palate, a kind of fleshy curtain suspended from the back of the hard palate. The soft palate allows food and water to pass from the mouth to the pharynx; but it's a one-way street. Unlike most other mammals, the horse is unable to vomit.

The mouth is marvelously equipped for its work. In eating loose
4 feed, the horse uses his lips to pick up the material and his tongue

The digestive system of the horse is designed for grazing on grass. Sharp incisor teeth clip the grass and pull it into the mouth.

to move it back in the mouth. In grazing, he grips and cuts the forage with his incisor teeth. The food, moistened by saliva, is then chewed between the molars; the saliva not only assists swallowing, it also starts the digestive process through enzyme action.

A horse knows what tastes good to him. Small particles of food react on the tongue, in sensitive areas like our own taste buds.

By human standards, horses have excellent table manners. They eat quite slowly. Ordinarily, it will take a horse 15 or 20 minutes to eat a pound of hay, and five to 10 minutes for a pound of grain.

When thoroughly masticated, hay will absorb about four times its weight in saliva; oats absorb only their own weight. After the food has been chewed, the base of the tongue pushes it past the soft palate and on into the pharynx.

A horse's mouth is perfectly designed for drinking, too. He pulls the water in with an action quite similar to that of a suction pump, taking in about half a pint at every swallow.

The Pharynx

The pharynx is not only a help in digestion; it is also a safety valve. It's a short, tapering muscular tube connecting the mouth and the esophagus; and it's an air channel between the nasal cavities and the larynx. Through its muscular movements, it forces food down into the esophagus.

Because the trap-door of the soft palate has only one-way action, food and water in the pharynx cannot pass back into the mouth. When food might be rejected, it therefore goes from the pharynx out through the nostrils, giving the nose a unique double-duty.

The Esophagus

The esophagus is the highway to the stomach. It's a muscular tube that brings food down from the pharynx. It passes down the left side of the neck, through the thoracic cavity and the diaphragm.

The contractions of the esophagus work in only one direction. When food or water passes out of the nostrils, it usually means that the esophagus is blocked.

The Stomach

We would say that a horse has a trim figure. His stomach is really quite small for an animal his size. That's because the primitive horse was a slow but constant eater, and never handled any great quantity of food at one time. The capacity of his stomach is about four gallons, but it functions better when it doesn't have a peak load. Two-and-a-half

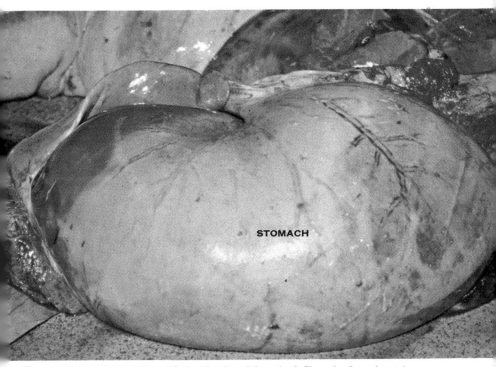

STOMACH

The equine stomach is small considering the size of the animal. Since the flow of gastric juice is constant, the horse should be fed more frequently than most animals.

gallons is about right. For this reason, it's important to feed a horse a little at a time, and feed him often.

The stomach roughly resembles the letter U. As food enters, it is arranged in layers, with the area near the small intestine filling up first. Digestion starts immediately. As the horse continues to eat, partially digested food passes into the small intestine; but no food passes from the stomach until it is filled to about two-thirds of capacity.

During a meal, as much as two or three times its capacity may pass out; the emptying process doesn't slow up until the horse stops eating. Normally, the stomach always contains some food, unless he has actually gone a day or two with no food at all.

Don't think of the stomach as a churn. Muscular action simply compresses and releases the contents, while the walls of the stomach are secreting gastric juices. An enzyme called pepsin changes protein into simpler compounds. The stomach digests but a very small portion of the horse's food; digestion takes place principally in the intestines.

A horse shouldn't have a lot of water following his meal. It disrupts the layering of the food, and may wash half the contents of the stomach into the small intestine. Unless he has access to water all through the day, better quench his thirst before you feed him.

Food leaves the stomach in the same order it enters. Feed hay first, so grain will have more time for the initial stages of digestion in the stomach.

The Small Intestine

Think of a horse's small intestine as a tube about 70 feet long and two inches in diameter. Its capacity is from 50 to 65 quarts. Located near the left flank, it's a series of folds and coils suspended from the loin region by a fan-shaped membrane called the mesentery. The first section of the small intestine lies in a U-shaped curve, apparently designed to prevent return of food to the stomach when the intestine is overdistended.

The small intestine is a fascinating chemical workshop. Starch which has not already been digested by saliva is changed into maltose by an enzyme in the pancreatic juice. Compound sugars are broken down into simple glucose-like sugar through the action of other enzymes; these simple sugars are then absorbed through the intestinal walls. Through the capillaries, they pass into the veins and on to the liver.

As with human digestion, starches are changed to glucose before entering the bloodstream. Small amounts of the compound sugars may possibly be absorbed unchanged; ordinarily, these are passed directly with urine, and not used in the body.

More enzymes produced by the pancreas, as well as bile from the liver, are added. During this phase of digestion, the food is liquid, and therefore passes through in a relatively short time.

The Large Intestine

The large intestine is quite an organization, consisting of five major components. These are the caecum, large colon, small colon, rectum and anus. They all have important jobs to do.

The caecum is a sac about four feet long, with a capacity of eight gallons. It starts high in the right flank and extends down and forward to the region of the diaphragm. The caecum and colon seem so large as to be almost out of proportion with the rest of the system. The extra size makes for slower passage of food, providing more time for bacterial action to break down the cellulose; cellulose is not affected by enzymes.

The cell walls of plants are largely comprised of cellulose. Because so much of a horse's diet is such roughage, his intake of cellulose is

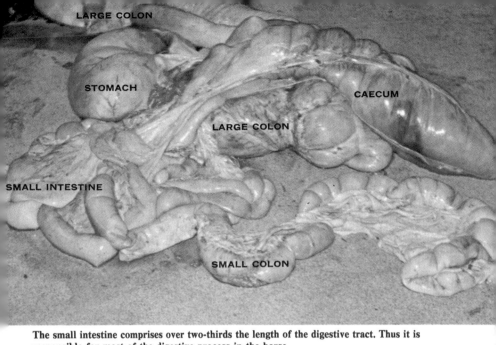

The small intestine comprises over two-thirds the length of the digestive tract. Thus it is responsible for most of the digestive process in the horse.

The caecum might well be described as a small equine "rumen." Here bacterial activity synthesizes many of the B-complex vitamins necessary for the horse.

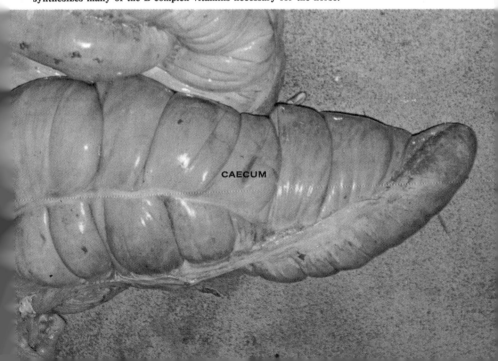

considerable. The caecum is sometimes called the water gut, because its contents are always fluid.

Extending from the caecum, and connecting to the small colon, is the large colon, about 12 feet long, 10 to 12 inches in diameter, with a capacity of about 20 gallons. It is usually distended with food. Further digestive and bacterial action takes place here.

The small colon is about 10 feet long and four inches in diameter, leading to the rectum. Here, most of the moisture of the food is resorbed, and the contents become solid. The last section of the digestive tract is the rectum, about one foot in length, between the small colon and the anus.

A series of veins, merging to form the large portal vein, collects most of the food from the intestines and moves it to the liver, the body's largest gland and principal chemical processing area. The liver manufactures bile, processes digested proteins, sugars, minerals and other food products, protects against various poisonous substances found in the digestive tract, destroys worn-out blood cells and helps to form blood proteins. ■

CHAPTER TWO

FUNDAMENTALS OF FEEDING

The modern horse is a lot bigger and works a great deal harder than his ancestors. The earliest known member of the family was the eohippus, about the size of a large dog. He lived on the softer parts of leafy vegetation, and apparently found it a good life. As he evolved and enlarged, he acquired an ability to eat the required wider variety of foods.

The wild horse lives on grass. He feeds almost constantly; otherwise, he rests, never getting much exercise. But domesticated horses are expected to perform various kinds of work; thus they need grain rations in addition to grass or hay. There are important differences between these two basics in his diet.

Grass is taken in slowly, and digested as eaten. But grain is a concentrated food, eaten much quicker but not digested as easily. It is important that grain rations be given often in small amounts. Grain swells when wet; if a horse is watered after eating grain, he may suffer colic; water him first.

The nutritive value of a horse's diet depends largely on the richness of the soil. Sometimes the area may be deficient in certain elements. Or the land may have been depleted through over-use. In such cases, a horse could eat adequate amounts but not get the food values he needs. Vitamin and mineral deficiencies must be made up through adequately formulated feeds or supplements.

As with human beings, a horse's diet depends on the individual. A lumberjack and a clerk don't need the same food; and there is a lot of difference between horses, too. A simple definition is that a horse should eat enough food to perform his work without losing weight. You'll find the correct amount to feed by learning your horse's habits and temperament. Perhaps your horse has some habits that are quite out of the ordinary; if they're not harmful, it may be easier to accommodate them rather than try to change them. Sometimes a horse can be as stubborn as a mule!

The purpose of a good diet is the same with all living creatures: to promote healthy growth; to replace worn-out body tissues; to provide fuel for normal body temperature; to supply energy for vital body functions; to maintain reproductive processes; to enable mothers to

The timing and methods of cutting and baling hay will determine its nutrient value. Here a Colorado farmer bales alfalfa hay.

produce milk.

Among horses, grass or other roughage, good water and salt make up the basic ration. But it is seldom satisfactory today, because of mineral deficiencies in the soil. Thus deficiencies are due to many factors: chemical fertilizers, over-working of the land, rainfall and climate conditions, time and method of cutting hay. Sometimes food values are reduced by 90%. So the horse owner cannot trust to Nature to provide a good diet.

Let's take the average situation of a horse used strictly for pleasure. A mature gelding, ridden only a few times a week for short periods, might be adequately fed on good green pasture from rich soil, as long as he has access to water and salt. But if he is younger and still growing, or the pasture is on poor soil, he will need more. He will need a mineral supplement containing cobalt, copper, iodine, iron, manganese and zinc, all of which can be supplied through a good salt-mineral block. He will

grass is 15% greater than when dried to hay; and young legumes like alfalfa are even more protein-rich than young grass. Also, young plants are soft and tender, having much less of hard-to-digest fiber and lignin.

There are some exceptions to the rule. Corn, small grains, sorghums and soybeans store large amounts of highly digestible nutrients in their seeds as they reach maturity; their nutrient count is highest when the seeds have fully developed.

Horse care means pasture care; the better the pasture, the better the horse. If grasses and legumes are cut frequently during the growing season, the total dry matter is less than when they are allowed to grow to normal hay stage. When cut, they present a smaller leaf surface to the sunlight; and there is a resulting reduction in the production of carbohydrates. Close grazing of forage will cause a similar reduction.

Among taller plants, too frequent cutting or too close grazing may seriously affect their vigor, depleting the reserve food in their roots and perhaps even causing them to die out. A system of crop rotation or alternate grazing is advisable.

Fertilizing pastures increases yield, maintains a longer growing period, produces feeds richer in proteins, minerals and vitamins. Plants are more succulent, more appealing to the animals. Types, methods and amounts of fertilizing have to be considered in connection with climate, natural fertility and other local conditions.

Since your horse will spend a good part of his life in the pasture, it ought to be comfortable for him. Shade, water and minerals should be provided. The land should be well-drained, to eliminate possible breeding areas for mosquitoes. Hazards such as stumps, pipes, old tanks or other objects should be removed. Under most conditions, depending on the climate, one or two acres of pasture will provide three to six months of grazing.

Range Feeding

On Western range lands, horses get so much nutrition from hay and grass that only small amounts of grain are needed. This is thrifty, because grain is more expensive. But it is important to prevent over-grazing. Horses bite off the plants close to the ground, and too much grazing weakens the roots, allowing weeds and coarser grasses to take over.

Additional damage is caused by the hoofs. They cut the young grass; and obviously, the damage is greater when horses are shod.

It usually takes about the same quantity of food to add a pound of weight to a horse as it does to add it to a cow. But because they graze closer and damage the grass by running, horses require a little more grazing area.

A horse on good pasture will do better than a stabled horse. Pastures should be rotated to prevent overgrazing.

Depending on growth in the area, from 15 to 50 acres of rangeland will be required for one horse. Of course, the area can be much smaller in irrigated or improved pastures. Range grasses drop sharply in protein, phosphorous and Vitamin A after growth has stopped, so supplements are necessary. These supplements are in the form of cottonseed cake, soybean cake or prepared pellets.

Basic Ration

Few investments will repay as much as a healthy, happy horse. And your horse's health depends, in large degree, on his rations. To be well-balanced, it should contain carbohydrates for body fuel, proteins as body-builders, and vitamins and minerals if he doesn't get them otherwise.

A good rule of thumb for a horse in moderate training is one pound of grain for each hundred pounds of horse. A horse standing idle should receive less; yearlings and pregnant mares are likely to need more.

The proper daily ration for your horse can make the difference between a strong, well-muscled horse above, and the scrawny, undernourished animal below.

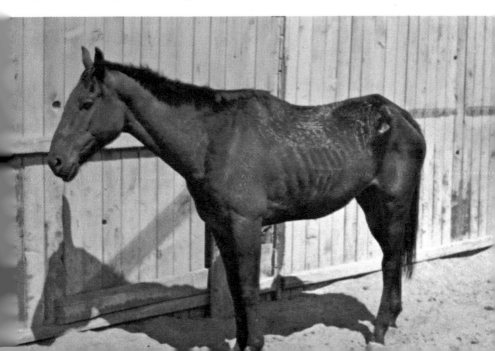

For mature horses in moderate use, here is one recommended daily feeding schedule: Morning; four pounds of crushed oats, one pound of barley, and seven pounds of mixed grass hay—timothy and clover. Evening; the same. This daily routine provides the horse with 14 pounds of grass hay, eight pounds of oats and two pounds of barley.

If this ration causes your horse to gain weight, then decrease the oats by a couple of pounds and increase the hay by the same amount. If he loses weight, reverse the process: increase the oats and decrease the hay.

Grains are mainly carbohydrates, supplying energy for muscular exertion. So they have a great bearing on the horse's weight. Most horses probably get too much grain and not enough work. But on the other hand, a hard-working horse will lose weight if he doesn't get enough grain. As with healthy people, there has to be a proper balance between the amount of food taken in and the amount of energy burned up.

The diet of an active horse should be 12 to 14% protein, whether he's a growing colt or a mature animal. Any less, and he won't perform at maximum efficiency. If there's any doubt, go ahead and feed some extra. If he gets more than he needs, the body converts the excess into fat for maintaining or gaining weight. ∎

NOTE

CHAPTER THREE

SUGGESTED FEED RATIONS

The question is, how much does a horse need to eat? The answer is another question. Which horse are you talking about?

He can require a lot or a little, and still be perfectly normal, depending on the circumstances. There are three basic factors in deciding the amount of feed he ought to have: his age, his size, and his work. Of course, there are other details to be considered, too; conditions that apply to stallions, broodmares and foals. A pregnant or lactating mare requires more, because she is "eating for two."

You will hear a lot about feeding a horse for "maintenance." This simply means enough to maintain his normal health and functions in periods of normal activity—grazing, chewing, lying down, getting up, walking about.

There is a great deal of difference between maintaining a horse and working one. "Working" him means imposing some duties in addition to his natural way of life; and, as with humans, the more work he has to do, the more nourishment he will require. Here, again, you

Suggested Daily Rations For 1200 lb. Lactating Mares

RATION #1	RATION #2	RATION #3
Legume Hay ....7 Lb	Legume Hay ....7 Lb	Legume Hay ....7 Lb
Grass Hay ......7 Lb	Grass Hay ......7 Lb	Grass Hay ......7 Lb
Oats ....13 Lb	Barley ....5 Lb	Oats ....15 Lb
Wheat Bran .....3 Lb	Oats ....9 Lb	Linseed Meal ....1 Lb
	Wheat Bran .....2 Lb	

Plus Free Access to Salt and Calcium-Phosphorus Mineral Supplement

Suggested Daily Rations For 400 lb. Weaning Foals

RATION #1	RATION #2	RATION #3
Grass Hay ......4 Lb	Grass Hay ......4 Lb	Grass Hay ......4 Lb
Legume Hay ....3 Lb	Legume Hay ....3 Lb	Legume Hay ....3 Lb
Oats ....3 Lb	Oats ....4 Lb	Oats ....5 Lb
Barley ....1 Lb	Wheat Bran .....1 Lb	Linseed Meal ....1 Lb
Wheat Bran .....1 Lb	Linseed Meal ....1 Lb	
Linseed Meal ....1 Lb		

Plus Free Access to Salt and Calcium-Phosphorus Mineral Supplement   **19**

The proper ration for any horse depends on the amount of work expected of him. Obviously, the race horses above will require a higher energy ration than the "weekend" horse below.

Suggested Daily Rations For 1200-lb. Pleasure and Show Horses

RATION #1	RATION #2	RATION #3
Grass Hay . . . . . 14 Lb Oats . . . . 5 Lb	Grass Hay . . . . . 14 Lb Oats . . . . 4 Lb Corn . . . . 1 Lb	Grass Hay . . . . . 14 Lb Oats . . . . 4 Lb Barley . . . . 1 Lb

Plus Free Access to Salt and Calcium-Phosphorus Mineral Supplement

---

Suggested Daily Rations For 1200-lb. Horses In Moderate Training

RATION #1	RATION #2	RATION #3
Grass Hay . . . . . 14 Lb Oats . . . . 11 Lb	Grass Hay . . . . . 14 Lb Oats . . . . 9 Lb Corn . . . . 2 Lb	Grass Hay . . . . . 14 Lb Oats . . . . 8 Lb Barley . . . . 3 Lb

Plus Free Access to Salt and Calcium-Phosphorus Mineral Supplement

---

Suggested Daily Rations For 1200-lb. Horses In Heavy Training

RATION #1	RATION #2	RATION #3
Grass Hay . . . . . 14 Lb Oats . . . . 16 Lb	Grass Hay . . . . . 14 Lb Oats . . . . 11 Lb Corn . . . . 5 Lb	Grass Hay . . . . . 14 Lb Oats . . . . 11 Lb Barley . . . . 5 Lb

Plus Free Access to Salt and Calcium-Phosphorus Mineral Supplement

---

Suggested Daily Rations For 1200-lb. Mares and Stallions In Service

RATION #1	RATION #2	RATION #3
Grass Hay . . . . . . 8 Lb Legume Hay . . . . 5 Lb Oats . . . . 8 Lb Wheat . . . . 2 Lb Wheat Bran . . . . . 2 Lb	Grass Hay . . . . . . 8 Lb Legume Hay . . . . 5 Lb Corn . . . . 4 Lb Oats . . . . 4 Lb Wheat . . . . 2 Lb Wheat Bran . . . . . 2 Lb	Grass Hay . . . . . . 8 Lb Legume Hay . . . . 5 Lb Oats . . . . 12 Lb

Plus Free Access to Salt and Calcium-Phosphorus Mineral Supplement

must also consider specific conditions, such as growth, reproduction and lactation.

A balanced diet is essential, whatever the circumstances: carbohydrates, fats, proteins, minerals and vitamins. In some Western and Southwestern sections, horses kept on pasture all year will get their maintenance ration from forage. They store up nutrients when the grazing is lush, then use the surplus when there is less grass. ■

CHAPTER FOUR

VITAMINS AND MINERALS

People have become extremely vitamin-conscious in recent years. We take our vitamins religiously, to be sure that any gaps in the diet are filled in; and we trust them to give us a greater measure of health and protection from disease. Vitamins are just as essential to horses as they are to humans.

The discovery of vitamins didn't come about until the early 1900's. Since that time, vast amounts of information have been compiled about them. But what are they?

The best definition seems to run like this: vitamins are nutritive organic substances which are essential in minute amounts for maintaining the life and health of animals and people. Vitamins which have been identified differ widely in chemical structure as well as function. Some are needed by only a few species, others by every living creature.

We are lucky in one respect. Some vitamins do not have to be supplied to us. We manufacture our own. Vitamin A, for instance, is needed by all animals, and can be made in the body from carotene contained in plants. However, if your horse doesn't get enough carotene in his natural feed, he will need supplemental Vitamin A.

Except for unusual circumstances, horses fed on well-balanced rations, including pasturage, will receive all the vitamins they need. But the amounts of particular vitamins in feed vary widely. That depends on the quality of the feed, stage of growth, and how the hay or other dry forage has been cured.

All green forage crops are rich in most of the required vitamins, except Vitamin D and Vitamin B-12. When animals are on pasture, the ultra-violet rays of the sun supply Vitamin D. For animals not on pasture, good hay and silage will usually supply enough of most vitamins.

Vitamin A

There is no vitamin more important to the health of your horse. Vitamin A is essential to the digestive, respiratory and reproductive systems. In mature animals, it is needed for normal maintenance, and also for growth, reproduction and milk production. Vitamin A itself does not exist in plant products. However, all green-leaved parts of plants contain certain yellow compounds known as carotene. Through action by the wall of the small intestine, and possibly the liver and other tissues, carotene is changed into Vitamin A for use by the animal.

The green leaves of plants contain more carotene than the stems; in alfalfa, six times as much. Thus alfalfa leaf meal is higher in carotene than meal made from the entire hay. Forage plants have more Vitamin A during their early stages, the amount decreasing as the forage becomes older. Little is left when the plants become dry and weathered. Animals kept on such forage too long may suffer severely from Vitamin A deficiency.

Legume hay, with a greater proportion of leaves, usually has more carotene than grass hay. When not too old, hay indicates its carotene content by its color and leafiness; but when it's been cut for a year, it is generally not an adequate source of carotene, regardless of its green color.

Vitamin A maintains the health of the mucous membranes, in the respiratory and other tracts, to help them resist infection. Deficiencies will make animals more prone to pneumonia.

Vitamin A is important in reproduction and lactation; lack of it affects the fertility of both male and female. In serious deficiency, there may be damage to the nervous system. The animal can develop a staggering gait, with eventual spasms or paralysis.

Usually, an early symptom of Vitamin A deficiency is night blindness, the inability to see in dim light. The condition is often cleared up when ample amounts are furnished; but extreme cases will sometimes result in permanent damage to the optic nerves. Other problems which may be caused by lack of Vitamin A are poor and uneven hoof development, certain leg bone weaknesses, and a picky, fanciful appetite.

When animals get enough Vitamin A, they store some in their livers and other tissues. How long it takes for a shortage to produce harmful results depends largely on how much is in storage. In mature animals, there may be enough reserve to last six months. Newborn animals have only a small supply, but the colostrum, or mother's first milk, is very rich in it.

Vitamin A supplements are widely available. There are also concentrates containing both Vitamin A and Vitamin D, made from cod liver oil and other fish oils. Carotene concentrates are produced from dehydrated alfalfa or vegetable wastes.

Vitamin D

Vitamin D helps to develop good bones and teeth, by aiding in the

Alfalfa leaves contain six times as much carotene as the stems. This girl is inspecting a
sample to determine the leaf content of the hay she is buying.

assimilation of calcium and phosphorous. Body requirements are much greater during growth, when the skeleton is being developed. Mature animals need much less, except during pregnancy and for milk production. Requirements are also less when there is enough calcium and phosphorous in the body.

Sunlight is the great source of Vitamin D. Ultra-violet rays convert small amounts of sterols in the skin and skin secretions into the vitamin. The greater distance the sun's rays have to travel, the less their ultra-violet content. So the sunlight in the tropics and at high altitudes is more potent, and it's more effective in the summer than in the winter, more at mid-day than in early morning or late afternoon.

Clouds, smoke and smog screen out some of the rays. Ordinary window glass eliminates practically all the ultra-violet rays, though special types have been developed which permit their passage.

The amount of Vitamin D is also affected by the animal's skin color; darker animals get less than light ones. But in general, any horse that's out in the sunshine during much of the growing season will get an ample supply.

A serious deficiency of Vitamin D in young animals may cause rickets. Even a slight shortage can retard growth and result in a weak skeleton, impaired joints and poor teeth. When pregnant animals are seriously deprived of the vitamin, their young are weak, subject to rickets, and may be born with malformations. It is also possible that the mother's skeleton will be injured.

Deficiencies can be corrected by feeding supplements rich in Vitamin D. The livers and some of the body oils of fish are treasures of the vitamin, and are widely used as sources for supplements. Irradiated yeast, produced by treating it with ultra-violet light, is also an effective supplement.

Vitamin E

Vitamin E is associated with an animal's reproductive qualities. Although the specific requirements are obscure, research has shown that lack of Vitamin E has hindered or prevented reproduction in some of the smaller animals.

A stable form of Vitamin E, called alpha tocopherol, increased the conception rate of mares and improved the breeding behavior of stallions. The vitamin also aids development and maintenance of muscle, and improves the performance of race horses.

Most livestock feeds supply Vitamin E. It is especially abundant in the green leaves of plants and good quality hay. Supplements are normally not needed, but are indicated during periods of stress, such as rapid growth, late gestation, intensive training or racing.

Vitamin D deficiencies may occur, particularly in younger horses. Most vitamin-mineral supplements contain more than enough Vitamin D to offset any deficiency. Here the supplement is added to the grain.

B-COMPLEX VITAMINS

Ten B-Complex Vitamins have been discovered, and there are probably more. Ordinary feeds contain a number of them, so that an adequate supply is usually available in natural rations. Synthesis of these vitamins takes place largely in the caecum and large intestine. These sources furnish a supply even when natural feeds might be lacking in the vitamins. Most green forages contain a good supply of all the B-Complex Vitamins except B-12.

B-1 (Thiamine)

Thiamine is part of an enzyme needed for metabolism of carbohydrates. It is widely furnished in stock feeds. Unmilled cereal grains are particularly rich in it, while white flour and polished rice contain little. It is also available in fresh green forage, well-cured hay and other quality dry feeds.

Thiamine also promotes appetite and growth, and is beneficial for reproduction. Supplements are usually not called for; if needed, they

Broodmares and other breeding stock may require Vitamin E supplementation. Good sources of Vitamin E are Wheat Germ Oil and Soybean Oil.

are easy to get in the form of dried brewer's yeast and dried fish solubles. Deficiency is indicated by lowered appetite, loss of weight, poor coordination and general nervousness. Prolonged deficiency may result in an enlarged heart.

B-2 (Riboflavin)

Riboflavin is part of an enzyme essential in oxidation of living cells. Its availability is much the same as that of thiamine. It is also synthesized in the caecum, and there is no need for supplements when horses have adequate amounts of good leafy forage. Deficiencies may lower the animal's appetite and growth rate. Prolonged lack may contribute to periodic ophthalmia, or "moon blindness."

Niacin

Niacin is also known as nicotinic acid. It is one of the B-Complex Vitamins, part of two enzyme systems essential to the metabolism of carbohydrates, lipid and protein. It is widely distributed in feeds, and additional amounts are very rarely necessary. 27

Pantothenic Acid

Necessary to the life processes, pantothenic acid is well supplied by alfalfa hay, green pasture, wheat bran and dairy by-products. Other good sources are yeast and cereal grains.

Choline

Choline is needed to build and maintain cell structure and metabolism of fat in the liver. It also aids in formation of acetylcholine, which makes possible the transmission of nerve impulses. It is available in sufficient quantities in the animal's normal diet.

Vitamin B-12

It stimulates appetite, increases utilization of food, increases growth rate. And B-12 is also important to normal reproduction. It is sometimes called the Animal Protein Factor.

There are several other B-Complex Vitamins, but they are not apt to be a problem with horses.

Vitamin C

Horses don't need Vitamin C as urgently as people do, but they do need some. It is also known as ascorbic acid. Animals get enough in their natural rations. Research has proved it beneficial in reproduction.

Vitamin K

Vitamin K preserves the clotting power of the blood and reduces bleeding from small wounds or other forms of hemorrhage. Deficiencies are quite rare, because it is available in fresh or dried greens, particularly alfalfa, and in fish meal.

MINERALS

Several minerals are essential in a horse's diet. These are the most important ones:

Salt

Composed of sodium and chlorine, which help transfer nutrients to the cells and remove waste materials. Sodium is important in making bile, to aid digestion of fats and carbohydrates. Chlorine is required in gastric juices for protein digestion. In cool climates, a long-term deficiency produces depraved appetite, rough coat, reduced growth of young animals and decreased milk production. There is little danger of overfeeding, unless a salt-starved animal is given too much all at once, or if sufficient water is not available.

Mineral supplementation is a good idea for all horses. Here the colt is getting his mineral from a combination salt-mineral block.

Calcium

Very important in developing bones and skeletal system. Grass hay and farm grains are usually deficient in calcium. Prolonged deficiency may result in rickets in young horses and a bone condition, osteomalacia, in mature ones.

Phosphorous

Important in the same way as calcium; the two must be maintained in the proper ratio. Especially vital when the animal isn't getting enough Vitamin D. Deficiency causes same problems as calcium deficiency.

Iodine

Needed by the thyroid gland to make thyroxin, which controls metabolism. Some U.S. areas, especially in the Northwest and around the Great Lakes, are deficient in natural iodine. It is vital that iodized salt be fed in these sections. Lack of iodine can result in stillborn foals. At best, foals will be very weak, unable to stand or nurse, more susceptible to navel ill.

Iron

Used to form hemoglobin, which enables the blood to carry oxygen. Also important to certain enzyme systems. Most common feeds have sufficient iron for basic needs. Leafy forages and legume seeds are iron-rich. If young animals are kept on milk alone for too long a time, they may develop anemia from lack of iron. Symptoms are loss of appetite with progressive emaciation; severe cases may be fatal.

Cobalt

Required by the bacteria that are so important in digestion of feed and in synthesis of B-Complex vitamins. Only a few parts of the country are naturally deficient. Trace amounts are sometimes added in deficient areas, and a drench is often administered to animals already seriously affected. Significant lack causes anemia.

Copper

Serves many of the same purposes in the body as iron.

Sulfur

An essential part of most proteins as well as certain vitamins and other compounds needed for the animal's vital processes. Required amounts are very small, and virtually every part of the country has enough sulfur in the soil.

Manganese

Needed by all animals in very small amounts. All ordinary feeds contain it, and most rations furnish enough for normal requirements.

Magnesium

Like manganese, magnesium is required by all animals in very small amounts, and is found in most ordinary rations. A very infrequent problem.

Potassium

Another trace mineral, available in the usual feeds.

Usually, a mineral deficiency means a soil deficiency. Since such problems are a matter of record, most horsemen will be aware of them, and protect accordingly by buying feeds or salt to which minerals have been added. If you have any doubt, better check with your veterinarian, experiment station, agricultural college or county agent. ■

CHAPTER FIVE

FEEDING THE FOAL, MARE, AND STALLION

It would be out of the question in your own family to feed the same amounts of the same food to mother, father and baby. And it would be just as out of place in the horse family. Let's look at the different members, and the different requirements; let's begin with the youngster.

The Foal

A foal makes the greatest growth of his life during the first 18 months. So the feed he gets at this time is especially important. His mother has carried and nourished him during about 11 months of pregnancy; he is born with his fundamental characteristics and conformation already built in. And, assuming he has a favorable heredity, he is born healthy.

His first nourishment will be the dam's colostrum, a specially rich milk yielded by the mother for a short time after birth. It's quite different from ordinary milk. It supplies antibodies to protect the foal against diseases, especially of the digestive tract. For a day or two after birth, these antibodies pass through the foal's intestinal wall and directly into the blood stream.

Colostrum is also very rich in protein, vitamins—especially Vitamin A—and minerals. Vitamin A is essential to promote the newcomer's growth; and if colostrum should not be available from the mother, supplements should be fed. He should also be fed cow's milk, preferably low in fat, if the dam is not able to supply him.

Between the ages of four and six months, the foal should be weaned. If the mare is bred again soon after foaling, or if mare or foal are not doing well, weaning might occur a little sooner. But when the dam is producing good milk and not carrying another foal, the youngster may well be permitted to suckle until he is six months old. Nursing beyond that time, particularly if the mare has been bred again, can sometimes lead to anemia in the mother.

Weaning should not be a major problem, but there are difficulties. The foal has to make some drastic changes in his feeding habits. He will also be emotionally disturbed by his separation from the dam. If possible, the separation should be made gradually; just keep the mare

The foal requires four to five gallons of milk per day. Therefore, creep feeding should be initiated as early as possible to ease the nutritional load on the mare.

away for increasingly longer periods when she's getting her exercise.

At weaning time, the two should be completely isolated from each other. If several foals can be weaned at once, they can keep each other company. When feasible, remove the mare and leave the foal in familiar surroundings, because he will be nervous and overactive, and might injure himself on unknown objects.

Long before that shattering experience, however, the foal has been started on feed. He is usually introduced to it between 10 days and three weeks. A good scientifically balanced ration added to good milk will get him off to a great start. When he is several weeks old, he will probably start nibbling from his mother's food box, if he can reach it.

Some time between four and six months, he should be put on creep feed. The creep feeder is a small enclosure with an opening too little for the mares to get in; but the foals can enter to enjoy their own special feed trough.

A good creep feeder can be constructed economically. Build a fence around the feed trough with openings at each end for the foal.

A good basic ration is crushed or ground oats and wheat bran. Another is, by weight, four parts of ground corn, three of bran and one of linseed meal. By the time the foal is weaned, he will probably be eating two or three, maybe even as many as five pounds of concentrates every day. He should also get some good legume hay as soon as he can eat it, and have good water always available.

After weaning, he should still have his creep feed, and around eight to 10 pounds of good hay every day. Alfalfa or clover, or a mixture of both, rate high in nutrients. To help the youngster put on some weight, supplement the rations gradually with a pound of oats and a pound or two of corn. Some breeders also feed a gallon or two of whole cow's milk, or add powdered milk to the ration, to assure a good supply of protein, calcium and phosphorous.

The first year of a foal's life is a period of furious growth. He will gain 50 or 55% of his total weight. His weight gain per pound of feed is almost twice what it will be in his second year.

When he graduates to the yearling class, he should be allowed to graze as much as possible; he will still require almost as much ration, though it doesn't need to be so high in protein.

At two years old, he will be within two or three inches of his mature height. On his fourth birthday, he will probably have achieved full height, though he may continue to grow in length. Between five and six he will reach full maturity. Any weight changes thereafter will result from variations in his diet or activities.

The Orphan Foal

If the mare should die, you will have to find some quick substitutes. If she dies before she gives colostrum to her foal, a veterinarian can provide a substitute by injection. Then, with proper care, the baby can be raised on cow's milk. It should come from a cow in the first part of her lactation, because that's when the fat content is lowest and the product most nearly resembles mare's milk.

A formula of one pint of milk, one-quarter pint of limewater and one teaspoon of sugar will provide two feedings at the start. Warm the mixture to 100 degrees F., and feed it to the foal in an ordinary nursing bottle with a large nipple. Clean and sterilize bottles and nipples. For the first few days, feed the foal every hour.

If the foal progresses satisfactorily, gradually increase the amount and lengthen the period between feedings until you're on a four-a-day schedule. After a few days, use whole milk instead of the formula, and teach the foal to drink from a suckle-pail instead of a bottle. At five or six weeks, sweet skim milk should be gradually substituted for whole milk; at three months, reduce the feeding schedule to three-a-day, and give the foal all the milk he will drink.

When he indicates he's interested in solid foods, give him a ration of crushed or ground oats, bran, a little linseed meal and legume hay. Plus allow him to graze on good pasture.

The Broodmare

Only about half the mares bred produce foals. The estimate is 40 to 60%. Why? It's a complex question, with many factors probably involved. But certainly improper nutrition is a leading cause. Good dietary practices should always be followed, but mares deserve some special care.

Keep them in good condition at all times. Prior to breeding season, be extra certain that they get the best possible rations along with needed supplements, and that they are adequately exercised.

Once the mare has conceived, she is obviously under the double burden of maintaining both herself and the embryo. And the foal-to-be grows more demanding all the time. If the mare's diet is lacking in any of the essential elements, they will be drawn from the mother's system by the foal, depleting her own supply. But when the pregnant mare has a full rich ration, the essential elements will be transmitted naturally to the infant, assuring him the best chance of a normal, healthy birth. A good diet also prepares the mare to produce rich, nourishing milk.

During the first half of her 11-month pregnancy, the mare should have the best roughage available, either rich, green grass or high quality hay. Thereafter, she should get at least two pounds of grain daily, along with necessary vitamins and minerals. After the sixth month, an adequate ration for an idle mare would consist of green grass, one pound of oats, one pound of cracked corn and supplements. If green grass is not available, substitute about 15 pounds of grass-legume hay.

The most rapid growth of the fetus occurs during the last third of pregnancy. So that's the time when protein, vitamins and minerals are especially important.

After she has foaled, withhold all grain from the mare's ration for two days. Then return to the two-pound ration, with a pound of dehydrated alfalfa pellets if needed.

During the next month-and-a-half, increase the grain gradually until the ration is made up of 15 pounds of hay, six or seven pounds of oats, four or five pounds of cracked corn, one pound of dehydrated alfalfa pellets and any needed supplements. If the mare is on green grass instead of hay, furnish only half of the specified grain ration.

Lactation, or milk production, is even more of a strain on the mare than pregnancy is. She requires almost twice as much digestible

In the first eight months the pregnant mare does not require a substantial increase in nutrition over maintenance requirements. However, an increase in nutrients is indicated during the last three months of gestation.

nutrients. Mares will produce from four to five gallons of milk every day on the average. To produce just one pound of milk, about 50 gallons of blood must circulate through the udder. So the process requires a tremendous amount of energy. Peak milk production is reached about the third month of lactation, then tapers off until the foal is weaned.

The Stallion

Ordinarily, the stallion has no special feeding needs. However, nutrition during the pre-breeding season is important, to make sure he is in top condition when it comes time for service. In effect, the better a stallion's ration, the better he will be able to function. His feed allowance should be regulated to keep him from putting on too much weight; a fat condition could lead to infertility. It's important to exercise the stallion, also, to keep him hale, hearty and vigorous. ■

GUIDE TO COMMON HORSE FEEDS:
CONCENTRATES

Feeds are divided into several categories. It's important for the horse owner to know something about the various classifications and the functions of each.

One of the basic groupings is concerned with fiber content and total digestible nutrients. These indicate the energy values of feeds. Concentrates are defined as feeds low in fiber—18% or less—and high in nutrients. Various grains and high-grade by-products fall in this class. These by-products include hominy feed, wheat bran, cottonseed meal, linseed meal, corn gluten feed, meat scraps and others.

Roughages, on the other hand, are feeds high in fiber but low in total digestible nutrients. Hay, corn fodder, straw and silage are in this category, along with some of the low-grade milling by-products like oat hulls, ground corn cobs and cottonseed hulls.

Roots are in a class by themselves. Based on the composition of their dry matter, they are more like concentrates. But being watery and bulky, with only a small amount of nutrients per pound, they are sometimes included as roughages.

Both concentrates and roughages are further classified on the basis of their protein content. Concentrates with less than 16% protein are called basal feed, and are comprised principally of the grains. If they have more than 16% protein content, they are considered protein supplements.

Among roughages, protein content is not so well identified, but the protein of most first-class roughages is of fairly good quality. The legumes usually have a higher content than the grasses, but their stage of maturity has a large bearing on this. Young plants are far richer, so timothy hay cut early would probably have more protein than clover cut late.

You will want to have a general understanding of other terms used frequently in the feeding of horses. The word "nutrient" means any food constituent, or group of them having the same general chemical composition, which aid in the support of life. The principal nutrients are protein, carbohydrates, fats, minerals and vitamins. Air and water would also fall within the broad definition. The phrase, "total digestible nutrients," sometimes abbreviated to TDN, means that part of a nutrient that may be digested and taken into the body. In common usage, it is applied only to protein, carbohydrates and fat.

A "ration" is the feed allowed an animal during a 24-hour period, whether it's fed at one time or divided into several feedings. A "balanced ration" is one that furnishes, in the right amounts and proportions, the nutrients required to nourish the animal properly for 24 hours.

The term "bulk" means the relationship between the feed's weight and volume. It varies considerably. A quart of oats, for example, weighs about one pound, while a quart of corn will weigh about one and three-quarter pounds; thus the oats have almost twice as much bulk as the corn. The amount of crude fiber content largely determines the bulk; as bulk increases, energy per unit of volume decreases. But a certain amount of bulk is required for proper functioning of the animal's digestive system.

Oats are one of the most popular feeds for horses. They are the standard by which other concentrates are judged. They are considered the safest of all grains; with their bulky hulls, they form an easily digested loose mass in the stomach, while heavier feeds such as corn, wheat and barley may have a tendency to pack; packing may lead to attacks of colic.

Oats also have enough protein so that, along with timothy or other good grass hay, they make a balanced ration for mature horses. They are, however, lower in total digestible nutrients than corn or barley, so that a ration of greater weight is required, particularly to keep work horses in condition. For very hard-working horses, it is better to furnish a mixture of oats with corn or barley.

Grinding or crushing oats is helpful for foals up to about eight months, and for horses with poor teeth. Don't furnish new or musty oats, because they might cause colic.

Barley is a very satisfactory feed. It should be crushed or ground, though not too finely. Being much heavier than oats, it should be mixed with a bulky feed, to avert the danger of colic. Some horse owners mix in about 25% of ground oats, or at least 15% of wheat bran or chopped hay. Barley is higher than oats in protein, and supplies considerably more total digestible nutrients than oats, although not quite as much as corn.

Next to oats, corn is the grain most commonly fed to horses. It is the most important crop in the United States, surpassing other cereals in yield of both grain and forage. Corn ranks high in both nutrients and net energy; it is very rich in nitrogen-free extract, which is nearly all starch, and is higher in fat than any other cereal except oats. It is also highly digestible, being very low in fiber. Corn is probably

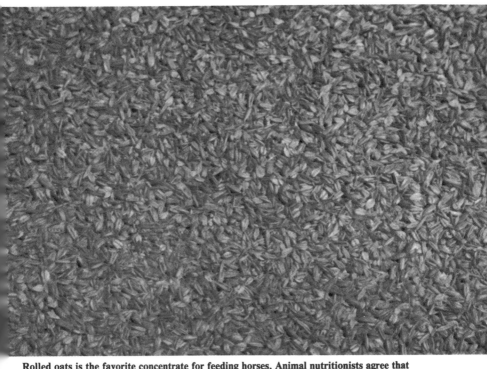

Rolled oats is the favorite concentrate for feeding horses. Animal nutritionists agree that it is the best horse feed you can buy.

the most palatable cereal, likely because of the high fat content and the fact that the kernels are chewed into nutty particles, tastier than more mealy cereals.

Because corn is so highly concentrated, take care not to over-feed animals in the summer; it may tend to add excessive fat. Compensate by feeding less corn and more hay. Corn is low in protein; for broodmares and growing horses, supplement it with a legume hay or protein additive.

Ear corn has some advantages over shelled corn. It keeps better; and since it takes longer to chew, it gets chewed more thoroughly. If you grind corn for horses with poor teeth, grind it coarsely to keep it from forming a heavy mass in the stomach. When the cobs are ground along with the corn, it makes a better meal because it provides needed bulk. Adding a little molasses cuts down on dustiness and adds some flavor.

Wheat is a very satisfactory substitute for oats; but it's not widely

Corn is high in energy but low in protein.　It does not supply enough bulk to make an ideal horse feed.

used because of the cost. Under favorable conditions, and in wheat country, it may be just about as economical, however. Its protein content varies widely in different sections of the country, but it's higher than corn, and it supplies about as much in total digestible nutrients. Wheat should also be rolled or crushed, to make for easier chewing and digesting; and it should also be mixed with some bulky feed to prevent colic. Ordinarily, wheat is used for no more than about 20% of the concentrate part of a ration.

Wheat bran is the coarse outer coating of the kernel. It's a by-product of milling and very popular as a feed. It's about twice as bulky as oats, and generally has a higher protein content than corn. In nutrients, it ranks only slightly below oats. Horses find it quite palatable, and it has a mild laxative power.

A bran mash is fed by many horse breeders once or twice a week during the winter, when no pasture is available.

Sorghum grains are popular in the lower Plains States and the Southwest. Due to lighter rainfall, they are widely grown in place of

Some commercial horse feeds contain molasses as an appetizer. However, molasses should not exceed 10% of the concentrate ration.

corn. Their protein is not of good quality, but they make a satisfactory feed when properly supplemented. The seeds are very small; they must be crushed or steam-rolled to make for easy chewing and to keep them from being swallowed whole. For bulk, mix with wheat bran, barley or oats. Sorghum may tend to induce constipation; wheat bran will help to prevent it.

Horses like the taste of molasses, and it's a good appetizer and conditioner. It has a mild laxative effect, and helps reduce the dustiness of some of the coarser feed mixtures. Cane molasses is often found to be a more economical source of energy than the standard grains. Proportion of molasses should probably not exceed more than about 10% of the concentrate ration.

You will want to know something about the natural protein supplements, and how they can be used to best advantage. Highest in protein content of all the common seeds used as feed is soybean meal. Both the beans themselves and the meal are fine supplements. It's a heavy feed, though, and not more than a pound a day should be used

Complete feeds are often produced in concentrated pellet form. A pelleted ration may cause the horse to chew wood in an effort to satisfy his need for roughage.

to balance a ration; soybeans should not make up more than a third of the concentrate mixture. Per pound of digestible protein, it is generally cheaper than linseed meal, and contains a better balance of amino acids.

Cottonseed meal and cake are widely used in the Southern and Southwestern states. Added to a low-protein ration, they are worth considerably more than corn or other grains, and are a valuable supplement in improving both the condition and the appearance of horses.

It is heavy like soybean meal, however, so don't feed more than a pound-and-a-half a day. Mix it with a bulky feed like oats, bran or corn-and-cob meal. Start your horse out with a small quantity of cottonseed meal, perhaps a quarter of a pound, and work up to the maximum amount. It can cause digestive problems if fed in excessive amounts.

Take some of the same precautions with linseed meal. Don't give more than a pound-and-a-half a day, mainly because it has a laxative effect. It is very effective in helping rundown horses with rough coats get back into condition, and in generally improving the bloom. Linseed meal has long been one of the most popular protein supplements. It's rich in protein, and has a strong taste-appeal for horses.

You may want to rely on some of the commercial feeds, compounded to provide a balanced ration. Basically, they are combinations of grains and grain by-products, proteins, minerals and vitamins, with a touch of molasses to improve the flavor. They are very convenient and easy to store. The ingredients provide adequate nutrition for most horses.

But don't rely entirely on them. Young, growing horses and lactating mares may need more protein than the commercial feeds supply. They are usually identified with their protein content, quantities of fat, fiber and minerals, such as calcium, phosphorous and others. Select carefully, and put them to the best use.

The complete pelleted feeds include both hay and grain. They are convenient, they make minimum demands for storage, and they are not dusty. Consider comparative costs; you may find pellets quite reasonable, especially when hay is expensive. One possible disadvantage is that the pellets offer so little bulk. Also they are sometimes blamed for bringing on cribbing in the horses. With so little roughage horses turn to chewing on wood in stalls, fences or other objects.

Again, so much depends on the individual horse and the individual owner. The horse owner must adjust to circumstances, and use his own judgment as he goes along. Knowing the essentials about concentrates should be helpful. ■

CHAPTER SEVEN

GUIDE TO COMMON HORSE FEEDS:
ROUGHAGES

Horses helped to build America; and hay helped to build the horses. It's for a very good reason that jokesters sometimes refer to the horse as a hay-burner; he has a lot of energy to burn, and hay is his fuel.

Hay is not the only fuel, of course. There are other roughages very important in a horse's diet. But throughout the temperate zones of the world, hay is by far the most important of the harvested roughages that horses eat.

Pasturage, silage and straw are also on the list of roughages. But many horse-lovers say that straw doesn't even belong there. It's a great deal less nutritious than hay; it should be made into bedding, not fed to horses.

A good quality hay has bulk, plus energy, protein, minerals, carotene and several of the B Vitamins. It should be made from plants cut at an early stage of maturity, when they are most nutritious. It should be handled and cured so that it's leafy and green, with soft-pliable stems, and hence more palatable to the animals. It should not be musty or moldy or dusty; it should be free of foreign materials such as weed or stubble.

There are two great hay families. They are the legumes, which produce seeds, and the grasses. The principal legumes used for forage are alfalfa, red clover and other clover varieties. Most commonly used grasses include timothy, prairie grass, orchard grass, bromegrass, Bermuda and Kentucky bluegrass. Various mixtures of legumes and grasses are also often fed.

Of all the common forages, legumes are richest in protein; so you don't need to feed so much protein supplement to make a balanced ration. Legumes are also high in calcium, and usually furnish all that is needed. They aren't very rich in phosphorous. But they rank high in Vitamin A and the highest in Vitamin D.

Alfalfa is one of the most widely grown tame hays in the United States. It's rich in protein, calcium and vitamins, and tastes good, too. But, you will have to limit alfalfa intake to keep your horse from eating too much. Not over one pound of alfalfa per 100 pounds of body weight should be allowed daily. Excessive amounts can lead to digestive

Alfalfa is one of the best hays. It is high in protein and nutrients. However, the average-sized horse should receive no more than ten pounds per day.

ailments.

Red clover is commonly grown in combination with timothy. The hay is second only to alfalfa in food values. Cut at the usual stage of maturity, red clover has about two-thirds as much digestible protein as alfalfa. But it furnishes slightly more total digestible nutrients, and therefore exceeds alfalfa slightly in net energy.

The grasses, like the legumes, are more nutritious when cut at young stages of growth. Mature and weathered, they are poor in protein, digestibility and phosphorous. They have practically no carotene. Even the early-cut grasses are not satisfactory substitutes for legumes; a mixed grass and legume hay is decidedly superior to a straight grass hay.

By far the most important hay grass in this country is timothy. It grows in the northern states, because it doesn't like the hot, humid areas. For mature horses, timothy hay is the standard roughage. It's usually freer of dust and mold than legume hay; and mature animals 45

Timothy is probably the most popular hay. It is cleaner than alfalfa and other legumes, but is not as high in protein and energy.

don't need as much protein, calcium and vitamins as growing horses and broodmares do. The latter will require a supplement.

In the Western states, native grasses are used for hay as well as forage. Grama and wheat grasses, bluestem and buffalo grass are the leading species, the value depending on climate and soil. Those that grow on mountain meadows and upland prairies are about equal to timothy in nutrition.

Orchard grass thrives mostly in a broad area south of the central corn belt. It is so called because it grows better in partial shade. Used mostly for pasture, often in conjunction with a legume, it also makes a good hay when cut at early bloom.

Smooth bromegrass, usually just called "brome," is used in northern and central states in legume mixtures for pasture, silage and hay. It's not only palatable, but remains so at later stages than most grasses. It makes a good hay; a mixture with legumes provides more total digestible nutrients.

Kentucky Bluegrass is popular in the areas where it is grown, and with good reason. If cut early in the spring, it may provide as much as 20% protein.

Bermuda is the most important pasture grass in the Southern states, but will not grow where winter weather is severe. Some varieties grow high enough to make hay. Coastal Bermuda is the most popular; it grows more in the fall, stays green longer, and resists leaf spot disease. Another tall variety is Suwanee Bermuda, suited for sandy soil. Bermuda is about equal to timothy in value.

In the Northern United States, Kentucky Bluegrass rates first. Well liked by all stock, it is rich in protein. Cut before heading out in the spring, it usually contains up to 20% protein when dried to hay. When kept growing through proper fertilization and management, it retains almost as much protein for many weeks. Yield is not abundant, however, due to its low spreading growth. ■

CHAPTER EIGHT

GUIDE TO FEED MANAGEMENT

Your horse is an individual. He eats for himself, not the whole species. Every day, you will be discovering something new and different about his personality. The sensible horse owner tries to understand his animal, and feed him accordingly. Study his habits. Consider his age, condition, working requirements and temperament. You will learn his likes and dislikes, and the kinds and quantities of feed he needs for good health. Soon, it will be almost an instinct with you to feed him properly. As you go along, try to bear these points in mind.

1. Feed at regular times every day, seven days a week. Feeding smaller quantities two or three times a day is beneficial. Divide the grain between the feedings. On a two-a-day schedule, feed one-third of the hay in the morning and two-thirds in the evening. On a three-a-day regimen, feed one-quarter of the hay in the morning, another quarter at noon, and the remaining one-half in the evening.

2. Feed only good quality grain and hay. Don't let your horse eat dusty, moldy or spoiled feeds.

3. The foundation of the ration should be a good quality hay, purchased as economically as you can for the type of horse involved. If hay costs are unreasonably high, reduce the hay and increase the grain.

4. Buy grain that gives your horse a good source of energy at the lowest possible cost. Buy protein on its cost per digestible pound.

5. Change rations gradually, giving your horse a chance to adjust to new feed a little at a time.

6. Never over-feed your horse. Horses get fat just like people. And overweight horses can founder.

7. Limit alfalfa to one pound for each 100 pounds of the animal's weight.

8. Vary grain portions with the amount of work the horse is doing. The harder he works, the more he needs.

9. Don't give a full feed to your horse when he's hot and tired.

10. Give him his grain after his hay.

11. Exercise him properly and regularly; that's just as important as a good diet.

Water

Water works wonders for all animals. We drink it simply because we're thirsty; and of course, your horse does the same thing. But it's interesting to note some of the miracles that ordinary water performs for us.

It dissolves nutrients or carries them in suspension from one part of the body to another. It reacts with many kinds of chemical compounds; complex food substances are broken into simple ones, then combined with water so they can be absorbed and utilized. Water fills the cells, and enables animals to hold their shape.

Water is the chief factor in temperature control; when warm-blooded animals become overheated, evaporation cools them. Water has a great capacity for absorbing heat; the watery tissues help to stabilize the temperature. A mature horse's body is about 50% water; a newborn colt may be as much as 80% water.

Obviously, an ample supply of good water is essential to your horse's health. He will drink around 10 to 12 gallons a day. Warm weather and hard exercise will naturally make him drink more. He will also want additional water if he's fed legume hay rather than grass hay.

Water him at regular times. Under most circumstances, he may drink before, after and during a meal with no problems. However, it is not wise to water a horse immediately after graining. And when he's been exercising vigorously and is hot, give him only small sips until he cools down.

Salt

Salt is another marvel working inside the bodies of living creatures, including people. It is said to be the most universal food of human beings, that's because we all must have it to live. Horses feel the same way about it.

Salt provides essential sodium and chlorine. It stimulates the secretion of saliva; it promotes the action of enzymes. It maintains the right osmotic pressure in the cells. Sodium maintains the body tissues; chlorine makes the hydrochloric acid in gastric juice. Salt regulates water metabolism and the passage of nutrients into the cells.

The body loses salt not only through urination but also through sweating. Hot weather and heavy exercise call for additional salt. A pound of sweat contains about two grams of salt. Horses normally need about two ounces of salt a day.

The common way of supplying salt is to put out salt blocks where the horse has free access to them. Salt may also be mixed into the ration; it should be no more than one percent of the ration weight,

Water is consumed by the horse at the rate of 10 to 12 gallons per day. Automatic water bowls assure a constant supply of fresh water.

perhaps only half that. A healthy horse won't eat excessive salt unless he's actually been deprived for some time. If there's a possibility he might eat too much, limit the amount available; otherwise, he may get indigestion.

You will have to use your own judgment in some matters. The amount of supplemental salt needed varies with the amount of salt contained in the feed and water. In some areas near the ocean, horses are said to need no supplemental salt at all.

Overfeeding

Horses can get fat. If you're an average American citizen, you may have had the problem yourself, or you know lots of people who have. It's no laughing matter, with either humans or horses.

Obesity can be serious in a horse. In a young, growing horse, overweight first puts an extra burden on the musculo-skeletal system; that makes his bones, joints, tendons and ligaments more susceptible to injuries. When the weight is disproportionate, he cannot move with the agility of a trim horse.

Overweight horses are prone to founder. Overeating grain will sometimes bring this about, and cause the horse to "road founder" from

Ordinary stock tanks may or may not contain fresh water, depending on the person responsible for them.

Commercial salt/mineral feeders are designed primarily for cattle, but are often used for horses.

The overweight horse will experience a number of problems - impaired reproduction, excessive stress, sometimes founder. Lush pasture may cause a horse to gain as much or more weight than the horse below.

In extreme cases founder may result in "snow-shoes" on all four feet. This condition can be treated by proper trimming of the hoofs.

excessive exercise. By upsetting the animal's metabolism, overweight can bring on azoturia, which causes stiffening of the joints and sometimes makes him go down in the hind quarters. Obesity also interferes with reproduction, and makes uncertain breeders of both stallions and broodmares.

Even the hungriest foal needs to have a "bridle" on his appetite. Grain contains some compounds that hinder absorption of calcium by the body; too much grain can thus bring on a calcium deficiency, no matter how much calcium you furnish in the diet. If this happens, the bones don't develop properly; in the more obvious cases, there will be enlarged joints, lameness and swelling of the legs.

And even in minor cases, troubles may come in later life, possibly causing the horse to be stricken with severe lameness. The correction of the problem in young foals is very simple: reduce the grain ration.

You cannot, of course, worry about every ounce of food or sip of water that goes into your horse. But you must be sensible about it, and manage his feeding in such a way that he will enjoy the best of health. ∎

CHAPTER NINE

NUTRITIONAL DISEASES

There are severe penalties for making mistakes in feeding the horse. And the sad thing is, you may make the mistakes, but the horse will have to pay the penalties. So you must be aware of some of the consequences of careless or uninformed feeding.

Azoturia

You have already heard something about azoturia. It isn't as common as it used to be, because its principal victims were work horses. It was popularly known as Monday Morning Sickness, Lumbago and Black Water. It isn't the great hazard it once was; but there's still enough of it around that a horseman should be on guard.

It results from disordered metabolic processes. It is probably due to overproduction of lactic acid in muscular activity. It almost always strikes suddenly. Any or all of the leg muscles may be affected; it's usually the hind legs and the large muscles of the loin and hindquarters. They become hard, stiff and painful to pressure. The horse's movements are uncoordinated; the muscles tremble. The pain causes him to sweat profusely. He may sit down on his haunches; he may go all the way down and then be unable to get up.

Breakdown of muscle tissues releases pigments into the blood stream, and they work their way into the urine; it becomes very dark, which explains the name Black Water. If the illness is not arrested, complete kidney failure may ensue. Don't try to move the horse. Get the veterinarian in a hurry.

Azoturia strikes most often when the horse goes back to work after a day or two of rest. Horses on high grain diets are most susceptible. But it is not confined to them. It is more common in winter and spring.

Absolute rest is a vital factor in treatment. While you wait for the vet, put heated cloths, blankets or hot water bottles on the swollen muscles. Reduce the diet; feed no grain. The veterinarian may give tranquilizers to relieve muscle spasm, cortisones to reduce inflammation, and thiamine to stimulate muscle metabolism. Pain relievers and alkalizers for neutralizing acidity in muscle tissues may also be indicated.

54   Horses which have suffered azoturia are predisposed to further

Azoturia is characterized by paralysis of the hind legs. It usually appears in the working horse after a few days rest on a full working diet.

attacks. They must therefore be fed lightly on grain and be exercised every day. Most cases can be prevented by basic good management. Don't overwork your horse, especially when he's not in top shape. And don't go too heavy on the grain. If your horse has been getting plenty of exercise, you can help clear up the digestive system by restricting his activity, cutting back his diet and feeding a laxative such as bran mash.

Colic

Colic is a common problem among horses, which could almost always be prevented by proper handling. The term is generally applied to abdominal pain and associated symptoms.

The horse will suffer pain, sometimes very great pain. Other symptoms include a distended abdomen, much stomach rumbling, violent rolling and kicking, sweating, constipation, and disinterest in eating or drinking. If the colic is not relieved, one disturbance may lead

55

to another. The discontinued muscular movements of the intestines may result in gas fermentation, extreme constipation, catarrh, inflammation, edema and hemorrhages.

Colic may be caused by sudden changes in feed, overeating and overdrinking, fatigue, defective teeth, spoiled or fibrous indigestible food, and exposure to abrupt weather changes. It's up to the owner to try to see that these conditions don't come about.

Make feed changes gradually. Limit your horse's drinking while he's cooling off. Check his teeth; perhaps inadequately chewed feed has caused a blockage of the gullet. Colic seldom occurs when proper practices have been followed. Follow these five rules for keeping colic away.

1. Give him enough but not too much of an adequate, nutritious diet; don't give him spoiled food or stagnant water.

2. Feed him from a manger; don't let him eat from the bare ground. Store the feed—especially grains, green feeds and new hay—beyond his reach. The principal cause of severe colic is uncontrolled eating.

3. When he's idle, cut down on his feed, particularly grain. When he's very tired, feed him lightly. Withhold both food and water when he's overheated.

4. If he's getting a lot of grain, divide it between morning and evening, and feed the grain after the hay.

5. Follow proper worming practices; blood worms can damage arteries and cause thrombo-embolic colic.

Severe colic may lead to a ruptured stomach or intestine, intestinal gangrene, abdominal cavity infection or toxicity, and result in the death of the horse. If your horse gets colic, give him quick first aid. Withhold all feed. Don't let him lie down. Walk him around the corral. If possible, place him in a large, well-bedded box stall, to prevent falling, kicking or rolling. And call the vet.

Heaves

You can refer to it as asthma, broken wind or the heaves. The textbook says it's pulmonary alveolar emphysema. By any name, it is a chronic respiratory disease of horses.

A persistent cough is among the first symptoms; it will intensify when your horse is exercised or exposed to dust. Violent paroxysms may occur following feeding or drinking cold water, after exercising, or when suddenly transferred from a warm barn into cold air.

Breathing is difficult because the tiny air sacs in the lungs have lost some of their elasticity. Breathing-in is easy and short, but expiration is difficult. The abdominal muscles try to compensate for the job the lungs aren't doing very well. There is a noticeable rolling

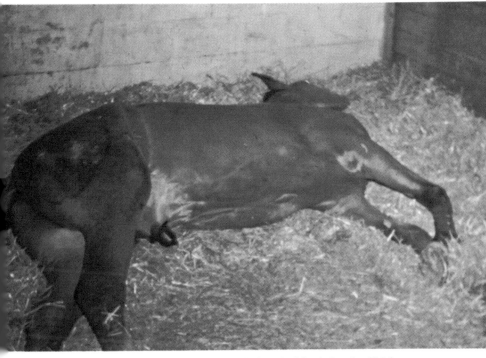

Colic is a catch-all name that refers to any pain in the horse's abdominal region. This horse is suffering from true colic—a pain actually caused by the digestive organs.

forward of the ribs under the skin. This causes a groove in the back of the ribs, called the "heave line."

Because of this extraordinary effort, horses eventually develop large barrel chests. This causes the ribs to be sprung apart, the muscles of the diaphragm to enlarge, and the development of a pot belly. The horse has no stamina, and often becomes unthrifty and remains in poor condition.

The excessive effort in breathing causes him to swallow great gulps of air, bringing on flatulence. Heaves may lead to chronic indigestion and diarrhea, frequently resulting in anemia and malnutrition. In severe cases, heart weakness and edema may follow, with swelling of accumulated fluids.

What causes the heaves? Infections, allergies, and perhaps other influences not yet discovered. Some cases follow respiratory infections. Most cases are aggravated by legume hays such as alfalfa or clover, especially if they're dusty or moldy; this strengthens the allergy theory.

What's the cure for heaves? There isn't any. But you can control its advancement by sanitary practices. If your horse shows any symptoms, have the vet look him over. If he's sick, particularly with a respiratory trouble, give him plenty of time to get well. Don't give legume hay to a horse with heaves; give him the best quality native meadow grass hay or prairie hay, free of dust and mold. Timothy hay is very good, and green pasture is best of all. Other beneficial foods are corn, beet pulp and sliced carrots.

There are special rations compounded for horses suffering from this disease. You may supplement them with vitamins and minerals. It's helpful to water the horse before feeding. Don't exercise him on a full stomach; give him three hours between feeding and exercise. And don't exercise him violently.

Various drugs may provide relief: antihistamines, cortisones and broncho-dilators. Commercial products containing stramonium are good; and good results are often obtained from a compound containing belladonna.

These are serious ailments you've been reading about, and the danger is you will be overwhelmed by the prospect of so much trouble with a horse. But your troubles will most likely be small ones. And you can avoid practically all of those simply by learning the essentials of horse feeding, and sticking with them.

Calcium Deficiency

Calcium deficiency, for example, can be a threat; but it need never be of concern to you if you make certain your horse is getting his calcium, and his body is utilizing it. Combined with phosphorous, calcium is the principal component of bones. Of all the calcium in the body, 99% is found in bones and teeth. Lack of calcium can bring on such diseases as rickets, osteomalacia, osteoporosis and osteofibrosis.

Rickets

Rickets is a disease of young animals. The bones don't grow and harden properly. Legs and ribs are most affected; knee and hock joints are enlarged. Joint surfaces may become rough and uneven, and the joints painful to move. Since he's hurting, the animal may lie down more than is normal. Weakened bones may make the legs bow.

These symptoms may be the first noticed. But they are actually evidence of an advanced stage. Usually, you will get earlier warnings from loss of appetite, weight loss, digestive disturbances or convulsions marked by rigid muscles and stiff legs.

Prevent rickets with adequate amounts of calcium, phosphorous
and Vitamin D. Heavy grain feeding may possibly lead to calcium

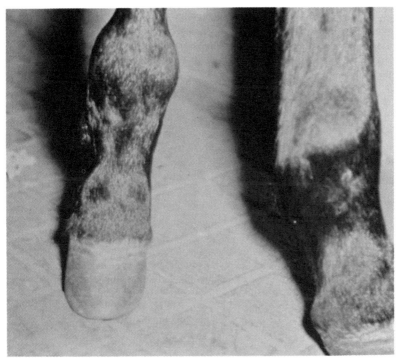

Rickets is caused by an imbalance of calcium, phosphorus, and/or Vitamin D. Visible symptoms are enlarged joints at the hock and knee.

deficiency. Natural feeds with good calcium content, properly fertilized pasturage or hay and specific mineral supplements should keep you from having to worry about rickets in your horse.

Iodine Deficiency

Iodine is another essential in the diet, but most horses get what they need from nature. Some areas deficient in iodine are reported to exist in Montana, Idaho, Oregon, Washington, Utah, Wyoming, North Dakota, Minnesota, Wisconsin, Michigan, California, Nevada, Colorado, Nebraska, Iowa and Texas. But find out for yourself by making local inquiry. If your horse doesn't get enough iodine, feed iodized salt.

Severe iodine deficiency causes enlargement of the thyroid gland, commonly called goiter. Lack of iodine interferes with normal reproductive processes, resulting in the birth of weak, deformed foals which often don't live. So just be sure your animal is getting his iodine from one source or another.

The same thing goes for salt, but perhaps a little more so. It is vital. If a horse doesn't get his salt quota, he will show a loss of appetite, lose weight, slow down in growth and develop a rough coat. If he has been lacking salt, don't try to make it up to him all at once; don't feed too much until he gets his system adjusted.

Vitamin A Deficiency

If your horse is fed only limited amounts of forage, or on feeds that have been stored so long that their natural carotene content has aged away, then he may not get enough Vitamin A. That's the vitamin that maintains normal eyesight, and keeps up the membranes lining the inside of the body. A shortage of it may reduce the ability to see in dim light. If the condition progresses, the eyes will water profusely, and the eyelids become inflamed and swollen. In prolonged cases, the outcome may be permanent blindness.

The skin may become dry and scaly, the hair coat quite rough. Mucous membranes lose some of their normal resistance to infection, inviting diseases to take hold. Reproductive disturbances may occur, along with respiratory ailments such as pneumonia or scours. Hoof development is abnormal, the hooves being rough, scaly, more liable to crack and chip.

But you'll have none of these troubles if you give your horse enough carotene in green, leafy hays, silage and green pastures. And if you think that isn't enough, feed Vitamin A supplements. Just one special note: during pregnancy and nursing, mares need five times the customary minimum requirement.

Urinary Calculi

A dietary problem seems to cause the disease called urinary calculi. This is a disorder of the kidney and urinary tract, in which stones, or calculi, develop and block passage of urine. It is believed to be caused by nutritional or metabolic disturbances. Many feeds and other factors appear to be related; and because the disease is not totally understood, it is sometimes unpredictable.

Some suggested causes are shortages of Vitamin A and D; an imbalance of calcium, phosphorous, magnesium and other minerals; a high silica content; and characteristics of some specific feeds. Your veterinarian will probably have to judge each case on its own circumstances.

A horse with urinary calculi will make frequent attempts to urinate, the results being scanty or none. In the early stages, there is restlessness; as the problem intensifies, the horse will walk with a straddling gait. Chronic obstruction may result in rupture of the bladder. Males are affected to a much greater degree than females.

Preventive measures include supplying your horse with plenty of drinking water and adequate amounts of Vitamin A. Establish a normal balance of calcium, phosphorous and magnesium; provide adequate exercise.

But once the stones develop, dietary treatment does not appear to have much value. Stones are sometimes removed from the urethra to give the animal relief; and muscle relaxants will often allow the stones to pass. ■

CONCLUSION

HORSE LAUGH

Horses don't really laugh, of course. But when you are well acquainted with a happy, healthy horse, full of spirit and good will toward the world, you're convinced that he would laugh if he could. Certainly, a well-fed, energetic horse brings joy and laughter to his people. Good feeding practices will bring you more satisfaction and enjoyment from your horse, and at the same time save substantially on your monthly feed bill.

You may have heard about the so-called "secrets" of successful feeding on renowned farms and ranches. Of course, there aren't any such secrets, just good old common sense and nutritional science. Having read this book, you may not know everything about horse feeding, but you know the essentials, and you know a great deal more than most people do. With this knowledge, you should be able to feed your horse every bit as well as the biggest horse farms in the country.

Remember, though, that while feeding is a very vital factor, it isn't everything. Your horse will not spend his entire life eating and drinking. You have to develop a management program that considers all his needs. Feeding has to be combined with training. That means plenty of exercise for every animal, but especially for brood mares, stallions and foals. If there's plenty of room to run, they'll usually manage to get enough exercise by themselves; but if a horse is stabled, then it's up to you to give him the necessary workouts.

Then, too, your feeding technique has to be part of a broader, overall health program. A complete equine health plan should include, in addition to proper nutrition, a disease prevention program, quarantine procedures, stable hygiene, immunization, regular internal and external parasite control.

And remember to rely on your common sense; your horse expects that much of you. Don't try to follow all the suggested rations in this book—or any book—unswervingly. They are not golden nuggets of wisdom; and maybe a lot of important things about horses haven't been discovered yet. Maybe you'll discover a few yourself!

Remember, too, that no two horses can be fed exactly alike with the same results. Differences in metabolism will prevent any two horses from doing equally well on the same ration. One horse may require considerably more feed than another, and demand a different kind of care. You must remain aware of these individual differences. ■